T4-AIN-708

**SHADOWLAND.** Contains material originally published in magazine form as SHADOWLAND #1-5 and X-MEN: CURSE OF THE MUTANTS SPOTLIGHT. First printing 2011. ISBN# 978-0-7851-4762-6. Published by MARVEL WORLDWIDE, INC., a subsidiary of MARVEL ENTERTAINMENT, LLC. OFFICE OF PUBLICATION: 135 West 50th Street, New York, NY 10020. Copyright © 2010 and 2011 Marvel Characters, Inc. All rights reserved. $24.99 per copy in the U.S. and $27.99 in Canada (GST #R127032852); Canadian Agreement #40668537. All characters featured in this issue and the distinctive names and likenesses thereof, and all related indicia are trademarks of Marvel Characters, Inc. No similarity between any of the names, characters, persons, and/or institutions in this magazine with those of any living or dead person or institution is intended, and any such similarity which may exist is purely coincidental. **Printed in the U.S.A.** ALAN FINE, EVP - Office of the President, Marvel Worldwide, Inc. and EVP & CMO Marvel Characters B.V.; DAN BUCKLEY, Chief Executive Officer and Publisher - Print, Animation & Digital Media; JIM SOKOLOWSKI, Chief Operating Officer; DAVID GABRIEL, SVP of Publishing Sales & Circulation; DAVID BOGART, SVP of Business Affairs & Talent Management; MICHAEL PASCIULLO, VP Merchandising & Communications; JIM O'KEEFE, VP of Operations & Logistics; DAN CARR, Executive Director of Publishing Technology; JUSTIN F. GABRIE, Director of Publishing & Editorial Operations; SUSAN CRESPI, Editorial Operations Manager; ALEX MORALES, Publishing Operations Manager; STAN LEE, Chairman Emeritus. For information regarding advertising in Marvel Comics or on Marvel.com, please contact Ron Stern, VP of Business Development, at rstern@marvel.com. For Marvel subscription inquiries, please call 800-217-9158. **Manufactured between 12/29/2010 and 1/26/2011 by R.R. DONNELLEY, INC., SALEM, VA, USA.**

10 9 8 7 6 5 4 3 2 1

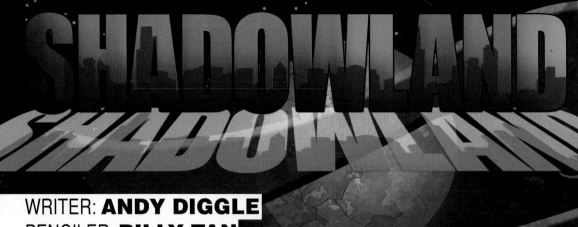

# SHADOWLAND

WRITER: **ANDY DIGGLE**
PENCILER: **BILLY TAN**
INKERS: **BATT** (ISSUE #1)
& **VICTOR OLAZABA** (ISSUES #2-5)
WITH **BILLY TAN** (ISSUES #3 & 4)
COLORISTS: **CHRISTINA STRAIN** (ISSUES #1-3)
& **GURU EFX** (ISSUES #1 & 3-5)
WITH **IAN HANIN** & **ANDREW DALHOUSE** (ISSUE #3)
LETTERER: **VC'S JOE CARAMAGNA**
COVER ARTISTS: **JOHN CASSADAY** & **LAURA MARTIN**
ASSISTANT EDITOR: **TOM BRENNAN**
EDITOR: **STEPHEN WACKER**

MATERIAL FROM *X-MEN: CURSE OF THE MUTANTS SPOTLIGHT*
WRITER: **JESS HARROLD**
DESIGN: **MICHAEL KRONENBERG**
EDITOR: **JOHN RHETT THOMAS**

COLLECTION EDITOR & DESIGN: **CORY LEVINE**
EDITORIAL ASSISTANTS: **JAMES EMMETT** & **JOE HOCHSTEIN**
ASSISTANT EDITORS: **MATT MASDEU, ALEX STARBUCK**
& **NELSON RIBEIRO**
EDITORS, SPECIAL PROJECTS: **JENNIFER GRÜNWALD**
& **MARK D. BEAZLEY**
SENIOR EDITOR, SPECIAL PROJECTS: **JEFF YOUNGQUIST**
SENIOR VICE PRESIDENT OF SALES: **DAVID GABRIEL**

EDITOR IN CHIEF: **JOE QUESADA**
PUBLISHER: **DAN BUCKLEY**
EXECUTIVE PRODUCER: **ALAN FINE**

# PREVIOUSLY

THEY ARE CALLED THE HAND – AN ORGANIZATION OF NINJAS, THIEVES AND ASSASSINS. ORIGINALLY BANDING TOGETHER 800 YEARS AGO TO FIGHT OFF THE OPPRESSIVE SYSTEM OF FEUDAL JAPAN, THE HAND TURNED TO CORRUPTION AND DARKNESS WHEN THE MUTINOUS SNAKEROOT CLAN SEIZED POWER.

OVER THE YEARS, THEY'VE COME INTO CONFLICT WITH MANY SUPERHUMANS — SPIDER-MAN, THE AVENGERS AND THE X-MEN TO NAME A FEW — BUT NONE OF THEIR FEUDS COMPARED TO THEIR WAR WITH DAREDEVIL. MURDOCK'S TIES TO THE HAND RUN DEEP; HIS MENTOR, STICK, DIED TRYING TO DESTROY THE HAND, AND HIS FORMER LOVER, ELEKTRA, SERVED THE HAND AS AN ASSASSIN FOR MANY YEARS, NEARLY LOSING HER SOUL IN THE PROCESS.

SO WHEN THE HAND SOUGHT OUT DAREDEVIL TO BECOME THEIR NEW LEADER, HE WAS UNDERSTANDABLY CONFUSED. HE INITIALLY REJECTED THEIR OFFER, BUT EVENTUALLY CONSENTED, PLOTTING TO USE THE ORGANIZATION AS A FORCE FOR GOOD. WHEN HIS ARCHENEMY BULLSEYE DESTROYED A CITY BLOCK — AND KILLED 107 PEOPLE IN THE PROCESS — MURDOCK RESOLVED TO TURN THE HAND INTO AN ARMY OF PROTECTORS.

OVER THE ENSUING MONTHS, THEY'VE CONFRONTED CRIME AND CORRUPTION ON THE STREETS OF NEW YORK — WITH BRUTAL FORCE. AS DAREDEVIL'S POWER WITHIN THE GROUP HAS GROWN, SO HAS HIS WILLINGNESS TO PUSH THE LIMITS IN ORDER TO KEEP THE PEACE. HE SOUGHT TO CHANGE THE HAND BUT IT APPEARS THE HAND HAS CHANGED HIM.

MATT MURDOCK DARED EVIL AND LOST. NOW PREPARE TO ENTER... **SHADOWLAND.**

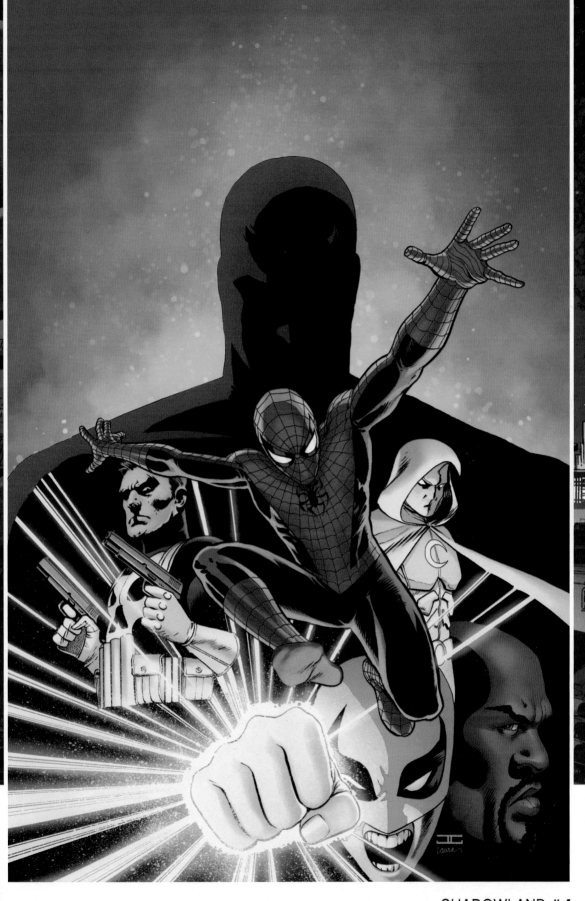

SHADOWLAND #1

SHADOWLAND

I THINK WE'RE READY TO BEGIN.

THE HIGH LINE--
PUNISHER

MIDTOWN--
KINGPIN

JAVITS CONVENTION CENTER

HAH! THIS'LL DO--PLENTY OF C.C.T.V. CAMERAS TO CATCH THE SPECIAL MOMENT...

JUST WATCH YOUR STEP, FELLAS--

AFTER ALL, YOU KNOW WHAT THEY SAY ABOUT PEOPLE IN GLASS HOUSES--!

AAAA--AAAH!

SKKASSSH!

WHUD

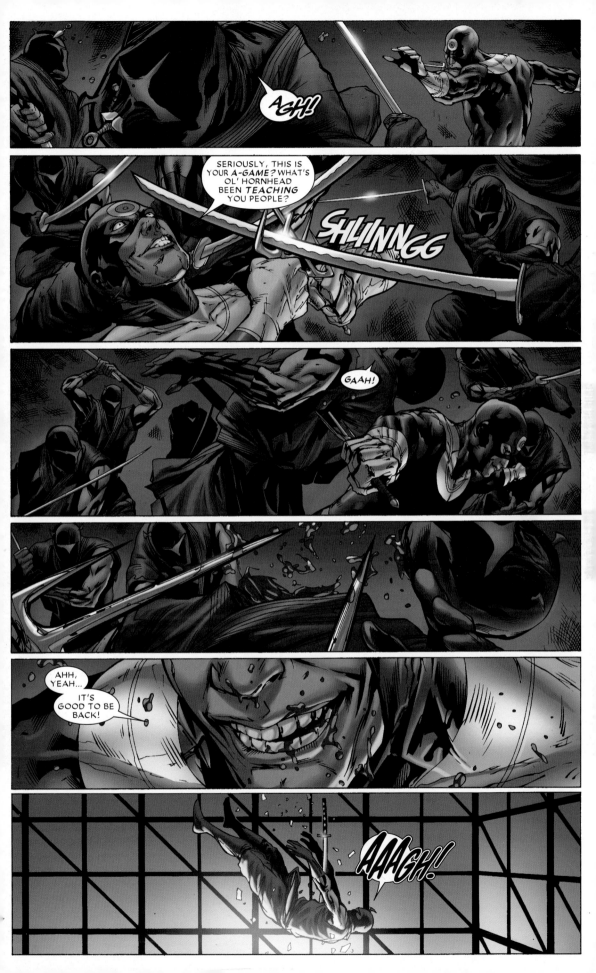

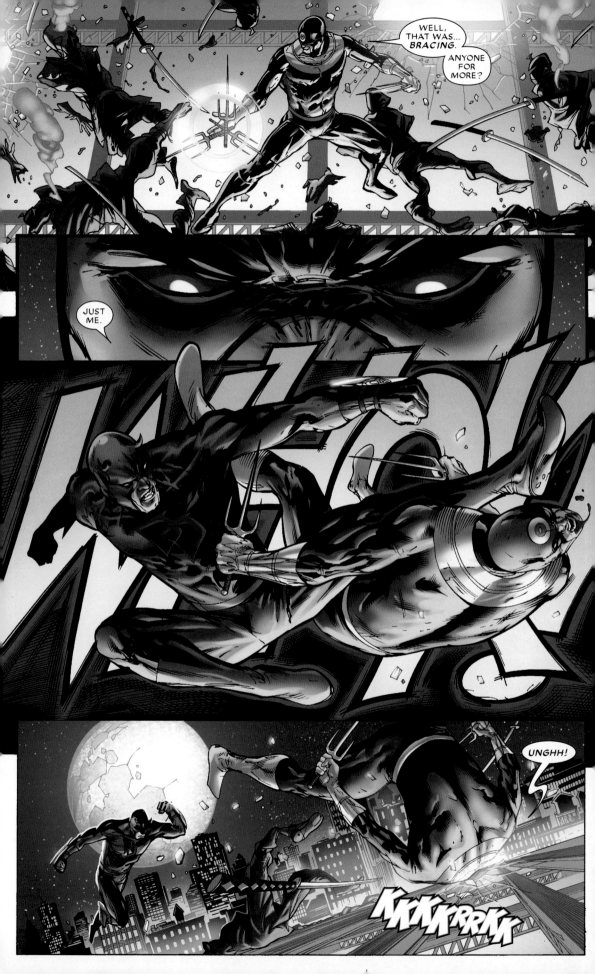

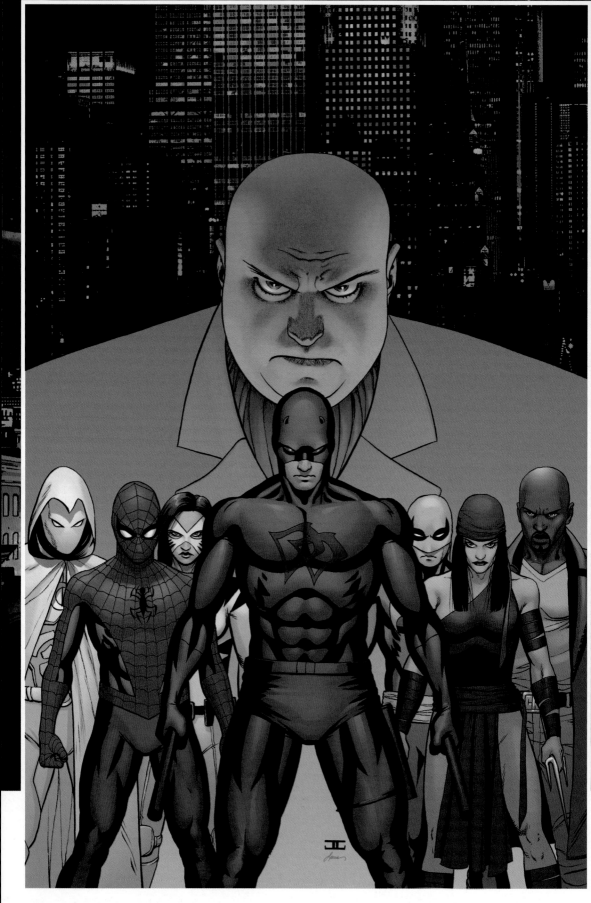

SHADOWLAND #**2**

SHADOWLAND, HE CALLS IT. AN HONEST-TO-GOD CASTLE, BUILT RIGHT IN THE MIDDLE OF HELL'S KITCHEN.

IT'S A DECLARATION OF INTENT. RIGHT ON THE BLOCK THAT *BULLSEYE* BLEW UP.

DAREDEVIL'S GOT EVERYONE RUNNING SCARED.

HE KICKED OUT THE COPS. DECLARED MARTIAL LAW. NOW HIS *NINJAS* RULE THE STREETS...

AND THEY CALL *ME* CRAZY.

THE SMALL-TIME CROOKS HAVE ALL CLEARED OUT, HEADED EAST-SIDE. ALL THE SMART ONES, ANYWAY.

BUT THE REST OF 'EM? THE ONES *THE HAND* ALREADY TOOK? NOBODY KNOWS WHAT HAPPENED TO 'EM...

IT'S LIKE HELL'S KITCHEN JUST SWALLOWED 'EM WHOLE.

MIDTOWN

SHADOWLAND #**3**

SHADOWLAND DUNGEON

IT MAY ALREADY BE TOO LATE FOR THAT.

MASTER IZO!

WHERE HAVE YOU *BEEN*...?

LEARNING THE *TRUTH*. THIS IS *MY* FAULT. ALL OF IT.

I STEERED MURDOCK TOWARDS THE HAND BECAUSE I THOUGHT HE COULD TURN THEM TOWARDS THE LIGHT. BUT I'VE BEEN A *FOOL*, A BLIND OLD FOOL...

BLIND TO THE *TRUE NATURE* OF THE HAND--AND THE ONE THEY *SERVE*!

MURDOCK IS NO LONGER HIMSELF, BUT AN UNWITTING PUPPET OF *SNAKEROOT*--THE SECRET CADRE AT THE HEART OF THE HAND!

ALL THIS TIME, ALL THEY NEEDED WAS A GOOD MAN --A *FLAWED* MAN, AN *ADEPT*-- TO ACT AS *VESSEL*.

A *VESSEL*? FOR *WHAT*...?

"A VESSEL FOR THE ONE WHO WAITS IN DARKNESS...

"WHO HUNGERS FOR THE *END OF HUMANITY* ITSELF...

"THE *BEAST* OF THE HAND!"

SHADOWLAND **#4**

BEAUTIFUL, ISN'T IT...?

THE STREETS *ABLAZE*. THE POLICE ARE TRYING TO CONTAIN THE RIOTS, BUT THEY'RE OVERWHELMED. *HELPLESS*.

THIS TURMOIL WE ARE WITNESSING IS MERELY A PERIOD OF *TRANSITION*, LADY BULLSEYE. THE DEATH OF THE OLD ORDER...

...AND THE BIRTH OF THE *NEW*.

SO YOU SAY. BUT I'M SICK AND TIRED OF WATCHING AND WAITING.

LET ME JOIN THE FIGHT.

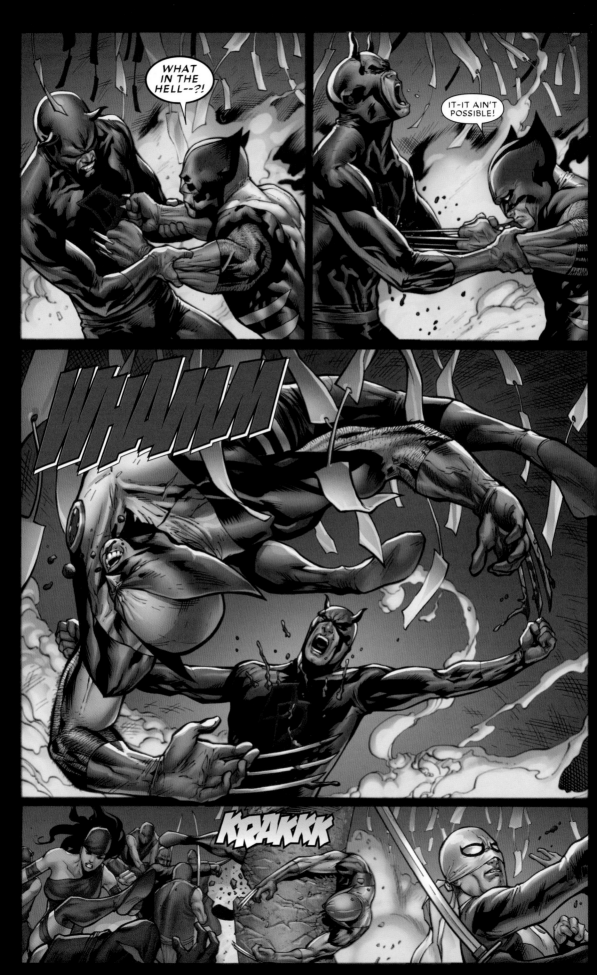

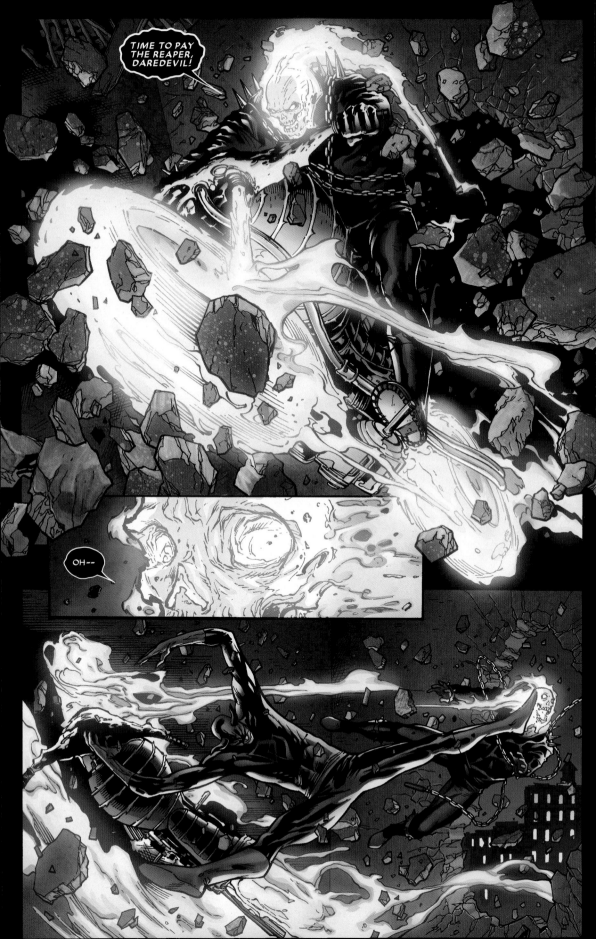

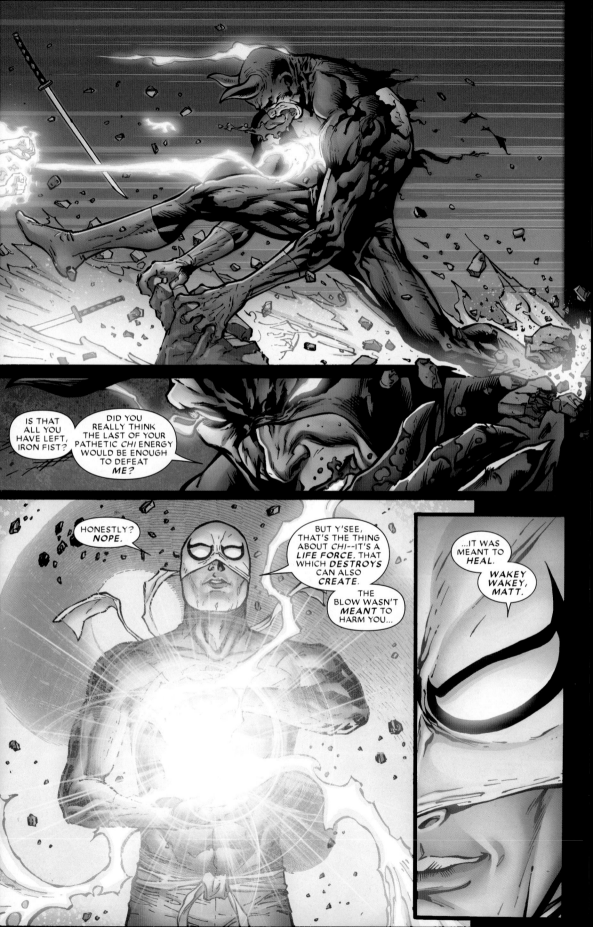

H-HELLO...?

HELLO? IS--IS ANYONE THERE...?

PLEASE, IT--IT'S SO DARK, AND I'M ALL ALONE...

DON'T COME CRYING TO ME.

M-MOM...?

DON'T CALL ME THAT. I DON'T WANT YOU. I NEVER DID.

YOU'VE THE *DEVIL* IN YOU, MATTHEW. WHY DO YOU THINK I LEFT YOU WITH THAT *VIOLENT ALCOHOLIC*...?

THAT'S YOUR *PENANCE*.

NNOOOOOoooooo...!

MATTHEW. GET OFF YOUR KNEES.

ELEKTRA...?

THE DARKNESS IS WITHIN YOU, MATTHEW. AND *YOU* ARE WITHIN THE *DARKNESS...*

*TRAPPED* WITHIN YOUR OWN *SELF-PITY.*

THE BEAST IS USING YOUR OWN SUBCONSCIOUS FEARS AGAINST YOU.

YOUR RAGE. YOUR GUILT. YOUR BLINDNESS TO EVERY POINT OF VIEW BUT YOUR OWN...

BUT YOU ARE NOT A CHILD. AND ONLY *YOU* CAN FREE YOURSELF.

B-BUT I-- I *CAN'T!* I'M *SCARED,* I-- W-WHAT CAN I DO...?

WAIT, WHAT--

WHAT AM I DOING...?

OH, MY GOD, WHAT-- WHAT IS THIS...?

I'M SORRY...

I'M SO SORRY--!

WHAT THE HELL...?

# LOST IN THE SHADOWS

## Writer Andy Diggle Finds Out What It Means For Daredevil When He Dares Evil...And Loses.

### By Jess Harrold

**W**hen Andy Diggle took over as writer of *Daredevil*, outgoing scribe Ed Brubaker left him a welcome present: a supporting cast of bloodthirsty ninjas, calling none other than Matt Murdock their boss. But faced with a moralistic super hero suddenly in charge of the murderous assassin cult known as the Hand, Andy was undaunted. After working on books including *Thunderbolts*, *Hellblazer* and *The Losers*, he's comfortable handling flawed heroes. And in Matt Murdock, he hit the motherlode.

*Shadowland* and *Daredevil* writer Andy Diggle.

After kicking off his run in *Dark Reign: The List – Daredevil*, Andy chronicled Matt's descent into the darkness in the pages of *Daredevil*. Matt's noble intentions of turning the Hand into a force for good – with their Shadowland fortress a symbol of hope to the people of Hell's Kitchen and beyond – turn to violence and chaos, the new addition to the skyline only a symbol of fear. Our hero's tragic fall is complete in the limited series *Shadowland*, where Matt does the unthinkable and slays his greatest enemy, Bullseye. As Hell's Kitchen burns, a costumed collection of Matt's most faithful friends battle to save him from the malevolent influence preying on his soul – and Andy sits at his computer and coughs. *Spotlight* caught up with the British writer while he composed the final draft of *Shadowland #5* in the midst of a bad cold. In between coughing fits, Andy filled us in about the comic-book tradition of making Matt Murdock miserable.

**SPOTLIGHT: Is there any super hero with a more messed-up life than Daredevil?**

Cover to *Shadowland #1* by John Cassaday.

**ANDY:** Good question! A lot of super heroes seem to be defined by how messed up their lives are. They tend to have these sad origin stories that screwed them up and made them become super heroes in the first place. Just look at what happened to Bruce Wayne's parents, or Frank Castle's family. They all seem to have loved ones killed in front of them, so they decide, "I must put on some tights and fight crime!" I think Matt Murdock's unique, in that he's not just driven by a single event in his childhood. He takes the whole world on his shoulders. He's always shouldering these burdens, refusing anybody else's help and just being bloody-minded about the way he pursues his personal war on crime. I think the writers have had a lot of fun piling more and more weight onto him. But you can't keep doing that forever. Eventually, something's gotta give. What we were trying to do with *Shadowland* was the culmination of all the misery piled into Matt's life by Brian Bendis, Ed Brubaker and then myself.

**SPOTLIGHT: *Daredevil* is unusual in that sense. Normally in super-hero comics, when a new writer comes on board, it either means a radical new direction or a reversion to the traditional status quo. But a succession of *Daredevil* writers have built on what came before, to the extent that Matt's descent into the darkness reads like a nine year epic, if not**

onger. Was building on that legacy important to you?

**ANDY:** Absolutely. Usually, I quite like shaking things up when I come onto a title. I like the idea of being able to reinvent and revamp and just generally change things up. But you don't want to reinvent Daredevil. You don't want to be the guy who goes in there and screws it up. Frank Miller already reinvented Daredevil, and we're all kind of standing on his shoulders. I'm not the guy who's going to come along and try and reinvent Frank Miller. Like you say, there has been this passing of the torch between writers to build this huge ongoing story, with each of them trying to leave the character in the most difficult plot situation possible for the next writer to deal with. When Bendis handed it over, Daredevil had just been outed as Matt Murdock and stuck in prison. I can just imagine the "Write yourself out of that one!" emails that passed between Brian and Ed. And, of course, when Ed passed it on to me, Matt Murdock had just agreed to become the leader of the Hand, his league of ninja assassins who had long been his greatest enemies. They're assassins, and Matt Murdock doesn't kill – it's like, OK, *why* did they choose him to be their leader?

**SPOTLIGHT: And that's where you come in!**

**ANDY:** Yeah, even before I got into the ramifications of Matt running his huge, multi-national criminal organization, I had to address that core question: Why did they choose him? I mean, he's a bit handy in a fight, sure, but there has to be more to it than that. I'm hoping, by now, a year later, the readers are learning what it was the Hand had in mind all along. But when I got handed that narrative hot potato, I couldn't just drop it and say, "Forget that. We're gonna take Daredevil into space now!" You've got to grab the ball and run with it

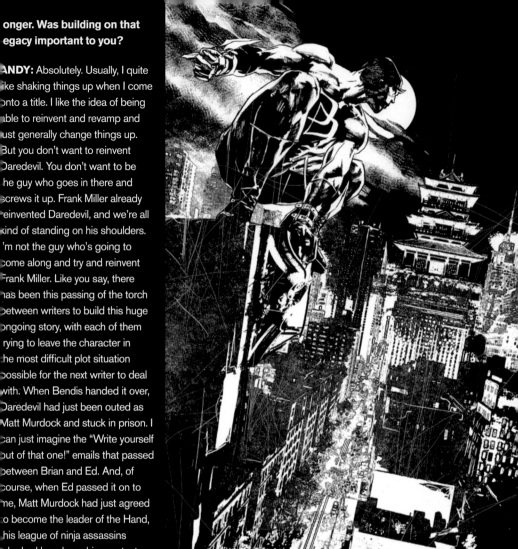

**SHADOWLAND: Artist Roberto De La Torre's striking black and white inked art from *Daredevil* #508.**

**SPOTLIGHT: And right off the bat (to mix sporting metaphors), you delivered a devastating event in *Dark Reign: The List – Daredevil*, where DD fails to prevent Bullseye from blowing up a tenement block, at the cost of innocent lives.**

> **"What we were trying to do with *Shadowland* was the culmination of all the misery piled into Matt's life by Brian Bendis, Ed Brubaker and then myself."**
>
> **– Writer Andy Diggle on the state of Matt Murdock**

**ANDY:** It was very much my first *Daredevil* issue and Marvel were keen to bring DD back into the wider continuity of the Marvel Universe. They're in the business of publishing comics set in a shared universe, but DD had been closeted away in Hell's Kitchen for years, wrapped up in his own affairs, and never got involved in wider events. Now, that's one of the things that DD fans really like. They like that he doesn't get too

**THE DEATH OF BULLSEYE:** Daredevil finally – and brutally – took down his nemesis in the pages of *Shadowland* and *Daredevil*. (Cover to *Daredevil* #508.)

mixed up in wider continuity – I think partly because that way they can kid themselves they're actually reading a crime comic, not a super-hero comic. But Marvel wanted to bring him back into the fold, and maybe up the action quotient a little bit. When they heard my plans for where I wanted to take DD as a character, they liked where I was going and asked me to make it even bigger and louder and darker.

**SPOTLIGHT: How would you describe Matt's motivations as he took the reins of the Hand?**

**ANDY:** His motivations as he took control were very much the belief that he could use them as a force for good. The first thing that he does is forbid them to kill anybody – which of course is instantly going to create all kinds of tensions within the Hand, because their point of view is, "Hey, dude, we're assassins! If we don't kill people, what the hell are we good for?" His idea was to use them kind of like an army – in the same way that at the end of the *Dark Knight Returns*, Batman forges the Sons of the Batman into a force for good. But they need a good man, a strong man, to control them. What Matt didn't know was that there was this hidden cabal at the heart of the Hand, secretly pulling his strings.

**SPOTLIGHT: If it could be summed up in a glib phrase, I guess it would be "The road to Hell is paved with good intentions."**

**ANDY:** It was very much that. When Marvel asked me to

do the crossover, I said, "OK, here's my five-word pitch: Daredevil is the bad guy." I flew over to New York for a pitch meeting with the editors; Joe Quesada and Dan Buckley were there, Steve Wacker and Axel Alonso, Tom Brevoort and Ralph Macchio – I was absolutely terrified! I was the new guy at Marvel; I hadn't grown up reading these characters – I was very much out of my element. I mean, Joe Quesada is a big DD fan. If I'm going to screw up, he's going to tell me I'm screwing up. But my take was, DD's the bad guy, and it's his own character flaws that lead him there. So yeah, very much the road to Hell being paved with good intentions, starting with that big bang: Why *wouldn't* he kill Bullseye? Some states have the death penalty. They'd have executed Bullseye long ago, if only they could keep him in prison long enough to do it. Killing Bullseye is kind of like the registration issue in *Civil War*: It's reasonable that some heroes would be for it and some would be against it. It's not an absolute black or white issue. But you can also see it as the beginning of the end for DD. Once he starts to compromise his moral code, it's a slippery slope. And the moment Matt does it, he's lost. It's not immediately apparent, but that's the point of no return for him.

**SPOTLIGHT: Indeed. Shadowland is billed as a battle for the soul of New York – but more directly it's Matt's soul that's at stake, from the Beast of the Hand. For anyone who hasn't come across him in earlier appearances such as *Elektra: Assassin*, what's his deal?**

**ANDY:** Everyone should read *Elektra: Assassin*! Basically, the Hand were created as servants of the Beast. That's what they were when Frank Miller was writing *Daredevil*. They served the Beast; that's what the Hand *is*. But that aspect of the Hand was gradually forgotten over the years, until they became just generic ninjas doing generic ninja stuff. And I thought that could work really well for me – because on the one hand, it slightly bugged me that everyone had forgotten about the Beast, and on the other hand it's perfect because I could have the Beast turn out to be the Big Bad, and it makes perfect sense in hindsight. Everyone should kick themselves and say, "I totally should've seen that coming," because it's all there in the old stuff. So it solved two plot problems right there: It gave me a villain and meant that Matt Murdock's fall from grace isn't entirely his own fault. But, on the other hand, it's not like he's possessed the whole time. The moment he's possessed by the Beast doesn't happen until after he's killed Bullseye. This thing might have been nudging at his subconscious, but that's a decision he made for himself. That act, that decision to step over the line, is what created a chink in his moral armor, so to speak, which is what allowed the Beast to get in in the first place. So Matt still damned himself.

**SPOTLIGHT: There's a brilliant little line on the Shadowland intro pages that sums it up: Matt Murdock dared evil and lost.**

**ANDY:** That wasn't me, that was Steve Wacker! I wish I could claim credit for it, but it's all Steve.

**SPOTLIGHT: Kudos to him! Now, you mentioned this was an opportunity to bring DD back to the Marvel Universe in a big way, but it was also your first big super-hero event, right?**

**ANDY:** Yeah, I guess it probably is. I've dabbled in super heroes before, but I very much come from the British comics tradition of *2000AD* and I didn't discover American comics until much later. I discovered Alan Moore's *Swamp Thing* as a teenager and followed it into what became Vertigo, but I never really followed super heroes particularly. It's required me to develop a whole new set of writing muscles. That unfamiliarity makes it quite difficult for me. I can't just jump in there. On the plus side, I guess it hopefully means I bring a fresh perspective to it. So *Shadowland* required me to do a lot of homework, but fortunately it wasn't one of these huge global events. It was all localized to New York. Marvel very much asked for it to be about the street-level characters.

**SPOTLIGHT: You mention the homework. Did you have to do a lot of reading when you took over the book?**

**ANDY:** Oh, yeah. I bought all the graphic novels and immersed myself in *Daredevil*. A lot of it I'd already read, like most of the Bendis stuff and the classic Frank Miller stuff. My all-time favorite DD story is *Elektra Lives Again*, which isn't really a Daredevil story at all. It's kind of a Matt Murdock story. But I always find when I'm writing these things that I'd much rather have the characters out of costume. I'd much rather write a story about Matt Murdock than a story about Daredevil, but that's just me and my aversion to tights!

**SPOTLIGHT: But you gave Daredevil new tights!**

**ANDY:** I did! I just said make the costume black, but Billy Tan took that and ran with it with the blades and the giant horns, and I'm like, "Yeah, cool, he looks like a bad guy now. (And it gave me the opportunity to put that Spider-Man quip in there about the black costume, too!)

**SPOTLIGHT: Spidey's just one of the "tights brigade" that show up in *Shadowland*. Was it difficult to balance that super hero aspect with the gritty stuff you mentioned that *Daredevil* fans love?**

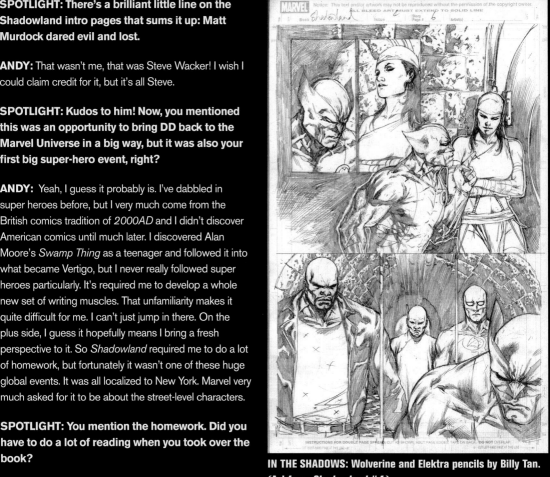

**IN THE SHADOWS: Wolverine and Elektra pencils by Billy Tan. (Art from *Shadowland #4*.)**

**ANDY:** *Shadowland* is a big colorful super-hero fistfight extravaganza, which is what super-hero readers want. Obviously, that's a broad generalization, but that's what you expect from a big super hero crossover book. Whereas in the *Daredevil* title itself, which I've been co-writing with Anthony Johnson, we've been very careful to make it a grimy, noir, urban crime book that's very character-driven. So hopefully the regular *Daredevil* fans get what they want, and the wider Marvel Universe fans get what *they* want.

> "...I never really followed super heroes particularly. It's required me to develop a whole new set of writing muscles."

**SPOTLIGHT: You've kept that tone in *Daredevil* by largely focusing on characters like Foggy and Dakota North...**

**ANDY:** I love those characters! I always wanted to write Foggy and Dakota teaming up. I loved the idea of them being a sort of comedy double act, Dakota being so much more competent on the street-level stuff. I mean Foggy's great in the courtroom or in the office, but I just love the idea of Foggy on the street being outclassed by Dakota. And I really loved the way Ed Brubaker wrote Dakota North. She's such a grown up, in many ways that

Matt Murdock isn't. Ed can write her as a strong woman without her being basically a man, or a bitch. There are so many subtle little touches. I would happily write Dakota North for the rest of my career, I think she's fantastic. I very much like the idea of taking B- and C-list characters that don't have a huge following, and freshening them up and approaching them in a new way. I would much prefer to do that than play with the A-list. Give me X-Men and I wouldn't know what to do with it. But give me six forgotten Wild West characters that nobody cares about and ask me to revamp them in the present day, and I'm a happy writer!

**SPOTLIGHT: I guess some of the characters you've been able to use in *Shadowland* – characters like Shang-Chi and Power Man and Iron Fist, who struggle to hold their own books – are a happy compromise between the two.**

# DRESSING THE DEVIL

**Artist Billy Tan.**

When the script for *Shadowland #1* called for a new costume for Daredevil, writer Andy Diggle made like a Rolling Stone and told artist Billy Tan: "Paint It Black." But the *New Avengers* and *Uncanny X-Men* penciler didn't stop there, whipping up new duds that fully fit the mission statement for *Shadowland*: Daredevil is the bad guy. *Spotlight* asked Billy about the unique test of turning Matt Murdock from fearless to fearful. "Redesigning an established character poses a much bigger challenge than designing a new one," he says, "since the artist is changing a costume that the fans are already accustomed to. And often, that is the character's classic look – so the pressure is on."

Billy handled the pressure well, designing the new outfit right on the page with no preliminary sketches. "It was definitely one of the quickest processes I've done. I didn't even have a design sheet for him. I just started drawing – and luckily, Andy and the editors liked what they saw. *Shadowland* has been a fun book to work on. The storyline is fast and furious, packed with action. It was my first event series, so there was quite a bit of pressure, and I was a bit nervous before I started. Luckily, I was blessed with a fantastic creative and editorial team on this book. There was a lot of relief after seeing the first finished issue!" Now feast your eyes on Billy's very first drawing of the new Daredevil suit, from *Shadowland #1* as Billy explains the diabolical details.

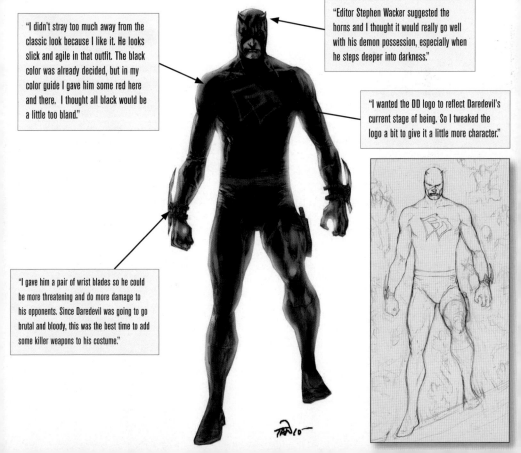

"I didn't stray too much away from the classic look because I like it. He looks slick and agile in that outfit. The black color was already decided, but in my color guide I gave him some red here and there. I thought all black would be a little too bland."

"Editor Stephen Wacker suggested the horns and I thought it would really go well with his demon possession, especially when he steps deeper into darkness."

"I wanted the DD logo to reflect Daredevil's current stage of being. So I tweaked the logo a bit to give it a little more character."

"I gave him a pair of wrist blades so he could be more threatening and do more damage to his opponents. Since Daredevil was going to go brutal and bloody, this was the best time to add some killer weapons to his costume."

*Shadowland* allowed you to use a lot of these super-powered friends Matt has built up over the years. If you can tell a lot about a guy by his friends, what do Matt's say about him?

**ANDY:** That he's a stubborn son of a gun! Matt's always been very single-minded, taking all of his burdens on to himself, refusing to have help with anything. But if you take that too far, what you end up being is a petulant whiner who sulks when he doesn't get his own way. I think there's maybe been an element of that in Matt Murdock's behavior. That kind of petulant child thing: Nobody understands me, leave me alone, I'll sort it out myself. Maybe there's a degree to which I wanted to teach him a lesson, humble him a little bit.

**SPOTLIGHT: And two friends you have really developed in *Daredevil* and *Shadowland* are Black Tarantula and White Tiger, kind of an angel and devil on Matt's shoulders. Do you have more plans for these guys after *Shadowland* – if they survive?**

**ANDY:** I wouldn't want to spoil the ending! But they've both got unfinished business: Black Tarantula feels guilty that he allowed White Tiger to fall the way she did. Because he was supposed to heal her, and he didn't realize she'd reverted. And she tossed him off a roof. But of course he's got a healing factor, so...

**SPOTLIGHT: Speaking of what happens next, the *Daredevil* title may be ending with #512, but we've seen some of the very cool Jock covers for the upcoming *Daredevil Reborn* you're writing. What can you tell us about it?**

**ANDY:** I can't really say very much at all because I don't want to spoil the ending of *Shadowland*. What can I say? It's about getting to the very heart of what drives the Daredevil character, what makes the character tick. But it's very different from a regular *Daredevil* book, not least in terms of the locale. Jock's doing his urban thing, skyscrapers and fires escapes and stuff, even though the story doesn't even take place in New York. It's about as far removed from the streets and rooftops of Hell's Kitchen as you can possibly get.

**SPOTLIGHT: And on interior art...?**

**ANDY:** I'm very lucky to be working with Davide Gianfelice, who did the first arc of *Northlanders* with Brian Wood and *Greek Street* with Pete Milligan. I love Davide's artwork. That first *Northlanders* volume is just

SPIDEY VS. PUNISHER: Shadowland promotional art by regular DD artist De La Torre.

unbelievably beautiful. He's up there with Ed Risso, I think.

**SPOTLIGHT: Lastly, we talked about that trend for writers on Daredevil leaving the next guy in a hole. Do you have something suitably devilish up your sleeve for when you pass on the billy club?**

**ANDY:** Yeah, Matt Murdock's gonna lose both his legs and become the new Stilt-Man! No, I'm not gonna deliberately make the new guy's life as hard as possible. Let's just say that, once I'm finished, *Daredevil* will be in a very good place to be relaunched with a clean slate at some point in the future.

Spotlight *looks forward to seeing what Andy has planned next in* DAREDEVIL REBORN•

SHADOWLAND #**1** 3<sup>RD</sup> PRINTING VARIANT BY BEN OLIVER

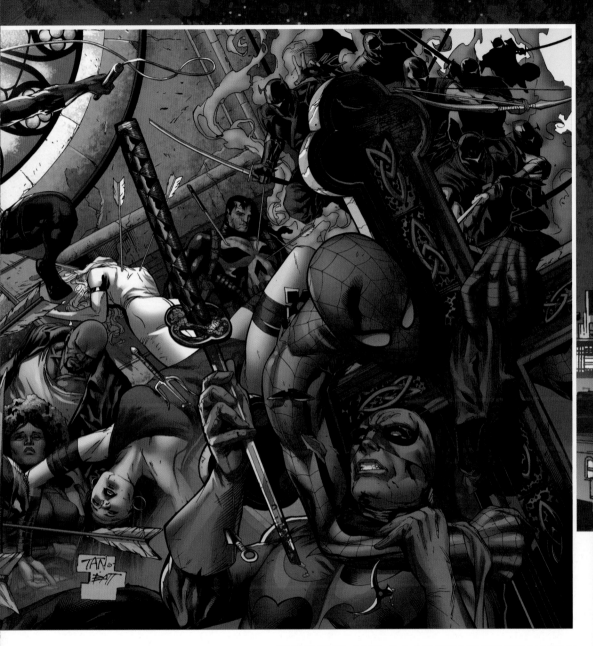

SHADOWLAND #**1** VARIANT BY BILLY TAN

SHADOWLAND #1 SKETCH VARIANT BY BILLY TAN

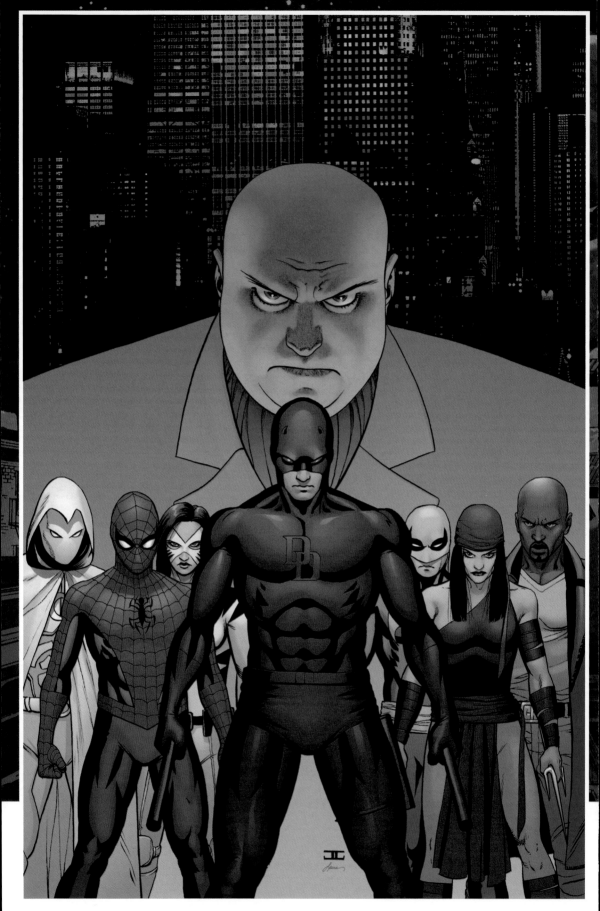

SHADOWLAND #2 VARIANT BY JOHN CASSADAY

SHADOWLAND **#3** VARIANT BY BILLY TAN

SHADOWLAND #4 VARIANT BY BILLY TAN

SHADOWLAND **#5** VARIANT BY BILLY TAN

SHADOWLAND **#5** VARIANT BY JOHN TYLER CHRISTOPHER